Contents

C000199657

Using this book   2

Practising times tables at home   3

Times tables sets 1–40   4–43

My times tables targets   44–45

Progress chart   46–47

Multiplication square   48

Times tables checklist   *inside back cover*

Using this book

This book contains 40 sets of times tables questions. Each set contains 25 questions worth one mark each and is designed to be completed in two-and-a-half minutes (150 seconds). This matches the pace of the Multiplication Tables Check, which takes place in Year 4.

What you will need
- a pencil
- an eraser
- a timer or stopwatch

How to use this book

Make sure you are sitting in a quiet place where there aren't any distractions.

Turn to **Set 1** on page 4. When you are ready to begin, start the timer.

Read each question and write the answer. You should not use a calculator. Work as quickly and as carefully as you can.

When you reach the end of **Set 1**, stop the timer. Use the **Multiplication square** on page 48 to check your answers. Then fill in the **Marks out of 25** and **Time taken** sections at the bottom of the page.

My times tables targets (pages 44–45)

Teachers and other adults can record your times tables targets and achievements on these pages.

Progress chart (pages 46–47)

For each set of questions, write your score in the box and colour the chart to show this score.

Multiplication square (page 48)

Use this to check your answers or to revise times tables.

Times tables checklist (inside back cover)

Once you are confident that you can recite a table in order, and multiply and divide by the number, put a tick in the relevant column in this checklist.

Practising times tables at home

A firm grasp of times tables is vital for providing a solid foundation for future problem solving. When children 'know their tables', their working memory is freed up to focus on other more complex tasks.

Keep practice short and sweet. Little and often gets results so try to make short bursts of practice part of children's daily routine.

Top tips

- Encourage children to use times tables in real-life contexts, such as when shopping, cooking or helping with DIY. For example, ask children to work out quantities for scaling up a recipe.

- Make copies of the **Multiplication square** on page 48. Ask children to spot patterns in the rows and columns and colour them in. For example, the multiples of 2 are even and always end in 2, 4, 6, 8 or 0, the multiples of 5 end in 5 or 0, the multiples that 2 and 5 have in common are 10, 20, 30, 40, and so on.

- Make a set of times tables flashcards for quick quizzes. Write the problem, such as 6 × 9, on the back and the answer, 54, on the front.

- Download a 12 × 12 grid from the Schofield & Sims website. Ask children to multiply numbers in the top row and first column together to fill in the grid.

- Make bingo cards with multiples on them. Call out different tables until someone gets a full house. For example, if you call out 6 × 4 then whoever has 24 on their card crosses it out.

- Throw two dice and ask children to write down the multiplication. Increase the challenge by using more dice.

- Play times tables tennis. Serve an imaginary ball by asking your child a times tables question. Your child returns it by answering as fast as they can.

- Show children a clock and ask them to multiply the numbers the big and small hands are pointing at together.

- Divide a pack of playing cards between you, so that you each get half the pack, and place them face down in front of you. Each player turns over their first card and the first person to multiply the two numbers together correctly gets both cards.

- Make times tables into raps, rhymes, songs or clapping games.

John Dabell, *teacher and author*

Set 1

$4 \times 4 =$	$3 \times 2 =$
$12 \times 6 =$	$6 \times 5 =$
$6 \times 10 =$	$8 \times 12 =$
$9 \times 7 =$	$12 \times 5 =$
$3 \times 4 =$	$6 \times 6 =$
$12 \times 12 =$	$4 \times 9 =$
$7 \times 11 =$	$2 \times 7 =$
$9 \times 3 =$	$12 \times 10 =$
$5 \times 9 =$	$2 \times 6 =$
$6 \times 4 =$	$8 \times 5 =$
$7 \times 7 =$	$12 \times 11 =$
$3 \times 3 =$	$6 \times 8 =$
$11 \times 8 =$	**Marks** out of 25 .... **Time** taken ....

Set 2

3 × 12 =	3 × 6 =
4 × 7 =	8 × 4 =
10 × 10 =	10 × 11 =
7 × 3 =	9 × 5 =
4 × 11 =	5 × 5 =
6 × 12 =	2 × 4 =
7 × 9 =	9 × 8 =
2 × 8 =	4 × 3 =
2 × 12 =	8 × 7 =
6 × 9 =	3 × 5 =
4 × 6 =	6 × 11 =
11 × 2 =	7 × 6 =
4 × 12 =	Marks out of 25 _____ Time taken _____

Set 3

5 × 12 =	3 × 3 =
9 × 2 =	5 × 9 =
10 × 3 =	4 × 5 =
4 × 9 =	3 × 7 =
6 × 8 =	11 × 11 =
9 × 12 =	7 × 7 =
5 × 6 =	9 × 11 =
9 × 3 =	4 × 12 =
7 × 12 =	4 × 4 =
6 × 9 =	7 × 9 =
5 × 7 =	8 × 5 =
9 × 8 =	11 × 10 =
6 × 6 =	**Marks** out of 25 .... **Time** taken ....

Set 4

$9 \times 9 =$	$11 \times 8 =$
$8 \times 6 =$	$8 \times 8 =$
$6 \times 5 =$	$2 \times 2 =$
$2 \times 6 =$	$2 \times 12 =$
$9 \times 10 =$	$6 \times 11 =$
$3 \times 9 =$	$7 \times 8 =$
$6 \times 7 =$	$4 \times 3 =$
$8 \times 3 =$	$7 \times 5 =$
$6 \times 4 =$	$8 \times 9 =$
$12 \times 4 =$	$2 \times 8 =$
$2 \times 9 =$	$3 \times 6 =$
$4 \times 7 =$	$10 \times 12 =$
$6 \times 12 =$	**Marks** out of 25 _____ **Time** taken _____

Set 5

11 × 3 =	9 × 3 =
3 × 12 =	7 × 8 =
3 × 6 =	9 × 2 =
11 × 2 =	8 × 12 =
4 × 6 =	4 × 11 =
6 × 6 =	7 × 7 =
7 × 5 =	8 × 10 =
5 × 4 =	4 × 12 =
12 × 5 =	10 × 6 =
9 × 8 =	10 × 11 =
9 × 4 =	3 × 7 =
5 × 5 =	11 × 9 =
7 × 9 =	**Marks** out of 25 _____ **Time** taken _____

Set 6

4 × 8 =	6 × 12 =
8 × 6 =	12 × 11 =
6 × 7 =	8 × 8 =
12 × 7 =	8 × 5 =
9 × 5 =	2 × 9 =
3 × 4 =	8 × 11 =
8 × 9 =	3 × 8 =
6 × 5 =	2 × 11 =
3 × 10 =	5 × 7 =
10 × 12 =	12 × 9 =
5 × 3 =	7 × 2 =
8 × 7 =	11 × 6 =
6 × 9 =	Marks out of 25 .... Time taken ....

Set 7

12 × 6 =	8 × 3 =
8 × 8 =	7 × 9 =
4 × 7 =	5 × 12 =
10 × 11 =	9 × 2 =
5 × 6 =	4 × 4 =
7 × 8 =	12 × 4 =
12 × 10 =	7 × 6 =
3 × 6 =	9 × 9 =
3 × 11 =	6 × 11 =
9 × 12 =	5 × 2 =
3 × 9 =	10 × 3 =
2 × 7 =	12 × 7 =
5 × 5 =	**Marks** **out of 25** _____ **Time** **taken** _____

Set 8

3 × 12 =	5 × 7 =
6 × 3 =	9 × 5 =
7 × 2 =	8 × 9 =
6 × 9 =	11 × 8 =
10 × 7 =	3 × 8 =
8 × 6 =	4 × 6 =
12 × 2 =	8 × 5 =
2 × 11 =	6 × 6 =
4 × 9 =	7 × 7 =
12 × 8 =	9 × 3 =
7 × 12 =	2 × 6 =
2 × 9 =	7 × 4 =
8 × 4 =	Marks out of 25 .... Time taken ....

Set 9

12 × 10 =	3 × 8 =
7 × 7 =	8 × 4 =
5 × 4 =	4 × 3 =
11 × 12 =	8 × 7 =
3 × 9 =	7 × 12 =
8 × 6 =	4 × 7 =
9 × 5 =	6 × 7 =
3 × 3 =	10 × 5 =
7 × 9 =	8 × 11 =
5 × 8 =	6 × 4 =
6 × 10 =	12 × 6 =
7 × 2 =	8 × 12 =
11 × 6 =	Marks out of 25 .... Time taken ....

Set 10

7 × 6 =	3 × 4 =
11 × 4 =	5 × 7 =
11 × 10 =	2 × 12 =
4 × 9 =	8 × 9 =
8 × 5 =	10 × 8 =
7 × 8 =	5 × 6 =
6 × 3 =	12 × 3 =
12 × 7 =	9 × 11 =
9 × 12 =	3 × 7 =
5 × 11 =	12 × 5 =
9 × 9 =	4 × 5 =
9 × 2 =	4 × 6 =
9 × 6 =	Marks out of 25 .... Time taken ....

Set 11

6 × 3 =	10 × 11 =
4 × 8 =	6 × 12 =
3 × 9 =	7 × 4 =
4 × 5 =	6 × 8 =
11 × 12 =	9 × 10 =
6 × 6 =	4 × 9 =
7 × 9 =	12 × 3 =
8 × 12 =	9 × 11 =
5 × 6 =	3 × 4 =
4 × 6 =	9 × 6 =
12 × 4 =	8 × 5 =
5 × 7 =	7 × 7 =
6 × 2 =	Marks out of 25 _____ Time taken _____

Set 12

2 × 9 =	12 × 11 =
8 × 7 =	10 × 6 =
6 × 5 =	9 × 12 =
2 × 12 =	8 × 3 =
9 × 8 =	11 × 11 =
6 × 4 =	6 × 9 =
7 × 5 =	12 × 7 =
8 × 4 =	9 × 9 =
11 × 3 =	8 × 2 =
5 × 8 =	10 × 8 =
8 × 6 =	12 × 10 =
11 × 2 =	12 × 6 =
5 × 9 =	**Marks** out of 25 .... **Time** taken ....

Set 13

 2.5 minutes

8 × 11 =	2 × 6 =
4 × 4 =	9 × 5 =
5 × 3 =	12 × 9 =
7 × 8 =	4 × 6 =
5 × 12 =	3 × 9 =
12 × 7 =	4 × 7 =
10 × 8 =	6 × 7 =
8 × 8 =	6 × 12 =
4 × 5 =	6 × 8 =
3 × 10 =	12 × 12 =
9 × 4 =	7 × 7 =
12 × 2 =	11 × 6 =
7 × 9 =	Marks out of 25 _____ Time taken _____

Set 14

 2.5 minutes

8 × 12 =	9 × 11 =
6 × 6 =	11 × 8 =
9 × 3 =	8 × 6 =
5 × 8 =	11 × 2 =
3 × 12 =	6 × 4 =
6 × 9 =	4 × 8 =
10 × 11 =	12 × 6 =
7 × 5 =	8 × 9 =
9 × 10 =	3 × 7 =
11 × 4 =	2 × 8 =
4 × 9 =	5 × 6 =
12 × 5 =	8 × 7 =
3 × 11 =	Marks out of 25 .... Time taken ....

Set 15

10 × 2 =	9 × 4 =
5 × 5 =	12 × 3 =
7 × 8 =	2 × 11 =
5 × 7 =	7 × 12 =
3 × 7 =	8 × 9 =
2 × 9 =	8 × 12 =
12 × 11 =	4 × 8 =
4 × 6 =	6 × 2 =
10 × 7 =	11 × 8 =
3 × 4 =	5 × 9 =
6 × 8 =	9 × 3 =
7 × 6 =	11 × 10 =
6 × 12 =	Marks out of 25 _____ Time taken _____

Set 16

9 × 9 =	3 × 9 =
11 × 4 =	6 × 5 =
10 × 6 =	8 × 8 =
3 × 8 =	6 × 4 =
10 × 9 =	4 × 12 =
11 × 7 =	12 × 5 =
6 × 11 =	8 × 10 =
7 × 7 =	3 × 2 =
7 × 4 =	9 × 8 =
3 × 12 =	11 × 11 =
9 × 2 =	12 × 7 =
3 × 3 =	6 × 6 =
2 × 12 =	Marks out of 25 .... Time taken ....

Set 17

8 × 11 =	4 × 7 =
9 × 4 =	7 × 6 =
8 × 4 =	6 × 8 =
5 × 5 =	3 × 9 =
11 × 6 =	5 × 10 =
4 × 12 =	9 × 7 =
8 × 8 =	7 × 3 =
7 × 8 =	4 × 6 =
8 × 12 =	9 × 9 =
6 × 5 =	11 × 4 =
8 × 9 =	10 × 8 =
12 × 2 =	3 × 3 =
12 × 11 =	**Marks** out of 25 _____ **Time** taken _____

Set 18

5 × 12 =	10 × 11 =
8 × 6 =	3 × 8 =
3 × 10 =	6 × 11 =
9 × 8 =	2 × 7 =
6 × 4 =	4 × 8 =
11 × 3 =	12 × 4 =
6 × 9 =	3 × 12 =
2 × 8 =	12 × 9 =
8 × 7 =	11 × 12 =
9 × 2 =	5 × 6 =
6 × 7 =	6 × 12 =
8 × 5 =	3 × 6 =
4 × 4 =	**Marks** **Time** out of 25 _____ taken _____

Set 19

11 × 5 =	12 × 4 =
8 × 9 =	6 × 9 =
12 × 11 =	12 × 6 =
10 × 9 =	4 × 5 =
11 × 10 =	5 × 12 =
8 × 4 =	7 × 12 =
3 × 6 =	4 × 7 =
8 × 5 =	8 × 11 =
12 × 8 =	5 × 3 =
6 × 8 =	2 × 9 =
7 × 6 =	6 × 4 =
8 × 7 =	7 × 2 =
4 × 3 =	**Marks** out of 25 .... **Time** taken ....

Set 20

$4 \times 9 =$	$8 \times 6 =$
$8 \times 2 =$	$6 \times 7 =$
$8 \times 8 =$	$4 \times 10 =$
$7 \times 4 =$	$12 \times 5 =$
$5 \times 7 =$	$9 \times 9 =$
$11 \times 9 =$	$7 \times 3 =$
$4 \times 4 =$	$6 \times 11 =$
$9 \times 5 =$	$2 \times 12 =$
$11 \times 8 =$	$3 \times 4 =$
$12 \times 3 =$	$7 \times 9 =$
$10 \times 7 =$	$9 \times 6 =$
$3 \times 8 =$	$4 \times 12 =$
$12 \times 12 =$	Marks out of 25 .... Time taken ....

Set 21

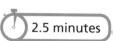

4 × 2 =	11 × 5 =
3 × 9 =	5 × 9 =
7 × 6 =	7 × 8 =
5 × 5 =	12 × 4 =
2 × 7 =	3 × 12 =
4 × 4 =	11 × 11 =
6 × 10 =	7 × 3 =
2 × 11 =	9 × 9 =
4 × 8 =	6 × 6 =
5 × 12 =	8 × 5 =
5 × 3 =	12 × 7 =
4 × 6 =	10 × 10 =
11 × 9 =	Marks out of 25 .... Time taken ....

Set 22

6 × 11 =	5 × 6 =
8 × 6 =	4 × 12 =
7 × 4 =	10 × 8 =
7 × 9 =	6 × 4 =
3 × 6 =	9 × 2 =
2 × 12 =	7 × 5 =
10 × 5 =	2 × 8 =
8 × 9 =	3 × 7 =
7 × 7 =	10 × 3 =
12 × 5 =	6 × 9 =
9 × 4 =	5 × 8 =
12 × 3 =	11 × 10 =
6 × 7 =	Marks out of 25 .... Time taken ....

Set 23

12 × 11 =	11 × 6 =
9 × 3 =	6 × 8 =
2 × 2 =	8 × 4 =
9 × 6 =	5 × 11 =
8 × 2 =	6 × 4 =
6 × 7 =	6 × 12 =
6 × 6 =	8 × 9 =
6 × 3 =	7 × 9 =
3 × 5 =	11 × 4 =
12 × 10 =	4 × 9 =
4 × 7 =	3 × 12 =
7 × 8 =	2 × 6 =
5 × 9 =	Marks out of 25 _____ Time taken _____

Set 24

4 × 4 =	7 × 6 =
3 × 9 =	7 × 4 =
4 × 12 =	10 × 10 =
7 × 12 =	5 × 8 =
7 × 5 =	8 × 7 =
6 × 9 =	8 × 12 =
4 × 11 =	5 × 6 =
9 × 4 =	2 × 3 =
11 × 9 =	12 × 5 =
9 × 12 =	5 × 5 =
3 × 8 =	5 × 3 =
9 × 7 =	3 × 6 =
6 × 11 =	Marks out of 25 _____ Time taken _____

Set 25

$2 \times 9 =$	$6 \times 4 =$
$12 \times 7 =$	$3 \times 12 =$
$12 \times 4 =$	$3 \times 6 =$
$8 \times 8 =$	$7 \times 9 =$
$9 \times 6 =$	$12 \times 8 =$
$5 \times 7 =$	$9 \times 8 =$
$4 \times 11 =$	$7 \times 6 =$
$9 \times 12 =$	$6 \times 10 =$
$2 \times 5 =$	$8 \times 3 =$
$4 \times 4 =$	$9 \times 5 =$
$12 \times 11 =$	$6 \times 6 =$
$2 \times 7 =$	$12 \times 12 =$
$11 \times 9 =$	Marks out of 25 _____ Time taken _____

Schofield & Sims ● My times tables book

Set 26

4 × 6 =	6 × 12 =
2 × 6 =	5 × 6 =
10 × 6 =	7 × 7 =
11 × 7 =	9 × 4 =
6 × 8 =	2 × 12 =
5 × 5 =	6 × 9 =
12 × 5 =	5 × 9 =
3 × 2 =	6 × 3 =
8 × 7 =	8 × 10 =
7 × 8 =	8 × 5 =
7 × 4 =	12 × 12 =
9 × 2 =	9 × 7 =
8 × 11 =	**Marks** out of 25 _____ **Time** taken _____

Set 27

5 × 3 =	7 × 12 =
2 × 5 =	4 × 7 =
10 × 6 =	9 × 12 =
6 × 8 =	4 × 11 =
6 × 7 =	9 × 9 =
3 × 6 =	6 × 9 =
2 × 3 =	5 × 7 =
5 × 5 =	12 × 8 =
2 × 9 =	4 × 6 =
6 × 11 =	3 × 8 =
6 × 2 =	3 × 7 =
8 × 4 =	11 × 5 =
2 × 10 =	Marks out of 25 _____ Time taken _____

Set 28

7 × 6 =	10 × 7 =
9 × 10 =	9 × 6 =
6 × 3 =	7 × 7 =
10 × 11 =	2 × 8 =
7 × 4 =	8 × 12 =
8 × 7 =	12 × 9 =
4 × 8 =	11 × 8 =
3 × 9 =	7 × 5 =
7 × 2 =	8 × 3 =
5 × 8 =	11 × 3 =
3 × 4 =	8 × 9 =
4 × 4 =	5 × 12 =
11 × 6 =	**Marks** out of 25 _____ **Time** taken _____

Set 29

2 × 7 =	11 × 2 =
7 × 5 =	12 × 5 =
10 × 2 =	5 × 6 =
11 × 8 =	2 × 6 =
3 × 12 =	9 × 4 =
10 × 9 =	12 × 7 =
8 × 12 =	10 × 8 =
3 × 9 =	4 × 11 =
5 × 3 =	4 × 7 =
12 × 4 =	6 × 8 =
7 × 9 =	4 × 6 =
5 × 10 =	11 × 11 =
12 × 9 =	Marks out of 25 Time taken

Set 30

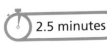

9 × 3 =	10 × 12 =
2 × 4 =	7 × 2 =
3 × 8 =	11 × 10 =
6 × 5 =	7 × 4 =
2 × 2 =	5 × 12 =
8 × 6 =	5 × 9 =
9 × 11 =	7 × 7 =
9 × 7 =	7 × 6 =
11 × 5 =	5 × 5 =
6 × 6 =	4 × 12 =
5 × 8 =	6 × 11 =
4 × 9 =	7 × 8 =
3 × 3 =	**Marks** out of 25 .... **Time** taken ....

Set 31

$11 \times 8 =$	$9 \times 9 =$
$5 \times 10 =$	$7 \times 3 =$
$3 \times 2 =$	$9 \times 12 =$
$8 \times 5 =$	$12 \times 7 =$
$3 \times 4 =$	$7 \times 8 =$
$12 \times 3 =$	$3 \times 9 =$
$10 \times 9 =$	$3 \times 11 =$
$12 \times 12 =$	$8 \times 3 =$
$7 \times 6 =$	$6 \times 9 =$
$6 \times 12 =$	$11 \times 11 =$
$3 \times 6 =$	$9 \times 7 =$
$9 \times 11 =$	$10 \times 6 =$
$8 \times 6 =$	Marks out of 25 .... Time taken ....

Set 32

10 × 4 =	3 × 12 =
9 × 2 =	5 × 12 =
7 × 11 =	6 × 3 =
9 × 6 =	2 × 6 =
4 × 9 =	11 × 6 =
3 × 8 =	7 × 9 =
9 × 3 =	3 × 3 =
9 × 5 =	7 × 12 =
12 × 8 =	5 × 8 =
8 × 7 =	6 × 4 =
6 × 5 =	9 × 10 =
6 × 7 =	9 × 8 =
4 × 7 =	Marks out of 25 .... Time taken ....

Set 33

 2.5 minutes

7 × 12 =	8 × 9 =
12 × 9 =	4 × 7 =
3 × 5 =	6 × 8 =
8 × 8 =	8 × 12 =
2 × 11 =	10 × 10 =
4 × 4 =	12 × 3 =
8 × 7 =	9 × 6 =
4 × 8 =	5 × 11 =
2 × 12 =	12 × 11 =
2 × 7 =	6 × 6 =
5 × 5 =	3 × 9 =
9 × 2 =	10 × 4 =
7 × 6 =	**Marks** out of 25 _____ **Time** taken _____

36 Schofield & Sims ● My times tables book

Set 34

5 × 6 =	12 × 8 =
2 × 9 =	7 × 3 =
11 × 4 =	5 × 8 =
5 × 10 =	8 × 6 =
6 × 4 =	9 × 5 =
9 × 3 =	2 × 8 =
11 × 11 =	7 × 9 =
7 × 7 =	11 × 12 =
6 × 3 =	9 × 9 =
9 × 11 =	5 × 7 =
4 × 12 =	11 × 7 =
3 × 4 =	11 × 10 =
12 × 6 =	**Marks** out of 25 .... **Time** taken ....

Set 35

12 × 7 =	7 × 4 =
6 × 6 =	8 × 8 =
5 × 9 =	7 × 9 =
6 × 12 =	12 × 8 =
9 × 10 =	5 × 5 =
9 × 12 =	8 × 6 =
8 × 11 =	10 × 3 =
6 × 7 =	11 × 12 =
12 × 2 =	9 × 4 =
9 × 9 =	10 × 7 =
2 × 9 =	10 × 10 =
3 × 8 =	8 × 7 =
6 × 3 =	**Marks** out of 25 .... **Time** taken ....

Set 36

5 × 10 =	8 × 4 =
8 × 9 =	9 × 7 =
6 × 11 =	2 × 8 =
11 × 11 =	8 × 3 =
7 × 8 =	3 × 6 =
12 × 10 =	6 × 7 =
3 × 5 =	4 × 9 =
10 × 4 =	6 × 8 =
7 × 7 =	8 × 5 =
2 × 12 =	5 × 6 =
4 × 5 =	8 × 12 =
3 × 7 =	5 × 2 =
6 × 9 =	**Marks** out of 25 .... **Time** taken ....

Set 37

3 × 11 =	7 × 7 =
8 × 10 =	7 × 5 =
12 × 8 =	7 × 9 =
10 × 9 =	7 × 8 =
5 × 9 =	6 × 7 =
8 × 6 =	4 × 9 =
6 × 3 =	12 × 7 =
5 × 8 =	3 × 12 =
7 × 4 =	12 × 6 =
5 × 6 =	11 × 4 =
3 × 5 =	11 × 12 =
4 × 2 =	8 × 3 =
4 × 6 =	**Marks** out of 25 .... **Time** taken ....

 2.5 minutes

6 × 9 =	5 × 7 =
4 × 4 =	12 × 4 =
8 × 7 =	12 × 12 =
9 × 12 =	9 × 7 =
10 × 11 =	3 × 6 =
6 × 5 =	4 × 3 =
4 × 8 =	3 × 10 =
2 × 9 =	9 × 8 =
3 × 7 =	9 × 3 =
8 × 2 =	7 × 6 =
4 × 5 =	12 × 2 =
11 × 11 =	10 × 4 =
6 × 6 =	**Marks** out of 25 .... **Time** taken ....

Set 39

4 × 6 =	9 × 9 =
3 × 3 =	3 × 8 =
10 × 9 =	7 × 11 =
9 × 7 =	12 × 4 =
11 × 6 =	5 × 8 =
4 × 8 =	6 × 10 =
9 × 8 =	5 × 9 =
3 × 5 =	7 × 5 =
11 × 10 =	8 × 12 =
3 × 4 =	8 × 6 =
3 × 9 =	10 × 7 =
5 × 6 =	9 × 12 =
9 × 4 =	**Marks** out of 25 _____ **Time** taken _____

Set 40

$2 \times 4 =$	$7 \times 12 =$
$8 \times 9 =$	$6 \times 6 =$
$12 \times 12 =$	$11 \times 2 =$
$7 \times 9 =$	$2 \times 9 =$
$9 \times 11 =$	$7 \times 7 =$
$12 \times 5 =$	$3 \times 10 =$
$7 \times 8 =$	$7 \times 4 =$
$6 \times 5 =$	$3 \times 12 =$
$8 \times 8 =$	$9 \times 3 =$
$11 \times 7 =$	$7 \times 6 =$
$11 \times 11 =$	$9 \times 6 =$
$5 \times 5 =$	$8 \times 3 =$
$4 \times 9 =$	**Marks** out of 25 _____ **Time** taken _____

My times tables targets

Date set	Target

Adult's comments	Date met

Progress chart

Write the score (out of 25) in the box provided to the right of the chart. Then colour the row next to the box to represent this score.

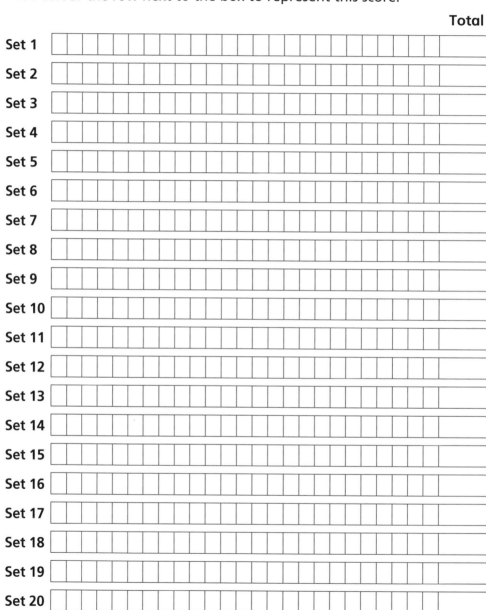

	Total
Set 1	
Set 2	
Set 3	
Set 4	
Set 5	
Set 6	
Set 7	
Set 8	
Set 9	
Set 10	
Set 11	
Set 12	
Set 13	
Set 14	
Set 15	
Set 16	
Set 17	
Set 18	
Set 19	
Set 20	

1 2 3 4 5 6 7 8 9 10 11 12 13 14 15 16 17 18 19 20 21 22 23 24 25   Score (out of 25)

Total

	1	2	3	4	5	6	7	8	9	10	11	12	13	14	15	16	17	18	19	20	21	22	23	24	25	Score (out of 25)
Set 21																										
Set 22																										
Set 23																										
Set 24																										
Set 25																										
Set 26																										
Set 27																										
Set 28																										
Set 29																										
Set 30																										
Set 31																										
Set 32																										
Set 33																										
Set 34																										
Set 35																										
Set 36																										
Set 37																										
Set 38																										
Set 39																										
Set 40																										

Multiplication square

This is a multiplication square. Use it to check your answers after you have completed each set of questions.

×	1	2	3	4	5	6	7	8	9	10	11	12
1	1	2	3	4	5	6	7	8	9	10	11	12
2	2	4	6	8	10	12	14	16	18	20	22	24
3	3	6	9	12	15	18	21	24	27	30	33	36
4	4	8	12	16	20	24	28	32	36	40	44	48
5	5	10	15	20	25	30	35	40	45	50	55	60
6	6	12	18	24	30	36	42	48	54	60	66	72
7	7	14	21	28	35	42	49	56	63	70	77	84
8	8	16	24	32	40	48	56	64	72	80	88	96
9	9	18	27	36	45	54	63	72	81	90	99	108
10	10	20	30	40	50	60	70	80	90	100	110	120
11	11	22	33	44	55	66	77	88	99	110	121	132
12	12	24	36	48	60	72	84	96	108	120	132	144